Little Voices
Classic Pops

GW00685370

NOVELLO PUBLISHING LIMITED
part of The Music Sales Group
London / New York / Paris / Sydney / Copenhagen / Berlin / Madrid / Hong Kong / Tokyo

Published by
Novello Publishing Limited
14-15 Berners Street, London, W1T 3LJ, UK.

Exclusive distributors:
Music Sales Limited
Distribution Centre, Newmarket Road, Bury St Edmunds, Suffolk, IP33 3YB, UK.

Music Sales Pty Limited
Units 3-4, 17 Willfox Street, Condell Park, NSW 2200, Australia.
This book © Copyright 2008 Novello & Company Limited.

Arranged by Barrie Carson Turner.
Edited by Rachel Payne.
Music processed by Paul Ewers Music Design.

Printed in the EU.

www.musicsales.com

Your Guarantee of Quality:
As publishers, we strive to produce every book
to the highest commercial standards.

The book has been carefully designed to
minimise awkward page turns and to make
playing from it a real pleasure.

Particular care has been given to specifying
acid-free, neutral-sized paper made from pulps
which have not been elemental chlorine bleached.

This pulp is from farmed sustainable forests
and was produced with special regard for
the environment.

Throughout, the printing and binding have
been planned to ensure a sturdy, attractive
publication which should give years of enjoyment.

If your copy fails to meet our high standards,
please inform us and we will gladly replace it.

I Have A Dream

Words & Music by
Benny Andersson & Björn Ulvaeus

Easy ballad style

you can take the fu - ture
push - ing through the dark - ness

ev - en if you
still an - oth - er

you can take the fu - ture
push - ing through the dark - ness

ev - en if you
still an - oth - er

Bb   Bb/C   C7

fail.
mile.

I be - lieve in

fail.
mile.

I be - lieve in

F

To Coda ⊕

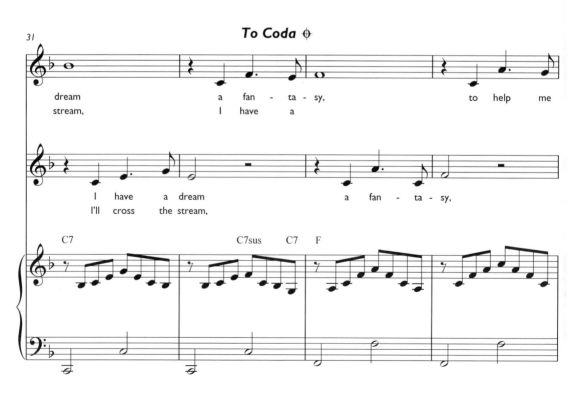

9

Mr. Blue Sky

Words & Music by Jeff Lynne

13

Hey you, with the pret - ty face,__ wel - come to the hu - man

Hey you, with the pret - ty face,__ wel - come to the hu - man

race. A ce - le - bra - tion, Mis - ter Blue__ Sky's up there wait - in' and to -

race. bra - tion, and to -

look a - round_ see what you do,__ ev - 'ry - bo - dy smiles at you.__

see what you do,__ ev - 'ry - bo - dy smiles at you.__

Fm   Eb   Db   Ab

Ba ba_____ ba ba ba ba.

Ba ba ba ba ba ba

Fm7/Bb   Cm   Cm/Bb

Ba ba_____ ba ba ba ba. Ba ba_____ ba ba ba ba, ah, ah.

ba. Ba ba ba ba ba. Ba ba ba ba ba ba, ah._____

Ab   Eb/G   Fm   Ebsus Eb   Db   Ab

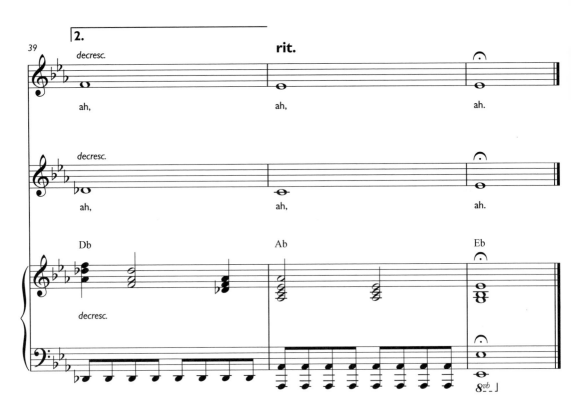

ah,   ah,   ah.

ah,   ah,   ah.

Db   Ab   Eb

decresc.

rit.

Morning Has Broken

Words by Eleanor Farjeon
Arranged by Cat Stevens

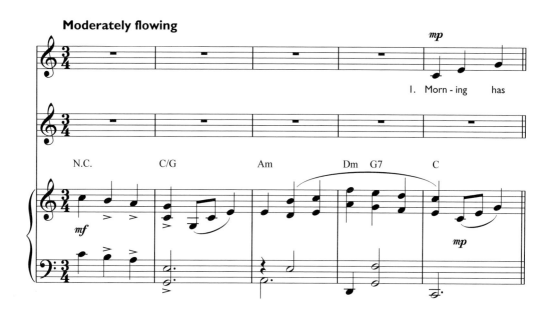

spo - ken like the first bird. Praise for the
dew - fall on the first grass. Praise for the
one light E - den saw play. Praise with e -

black-bird has spo-ken like the first bird.
like the first dew-fall on the first grass.
born of the one light E - den saw play.

Em   Am7   D7sus   D7   G   G7   C

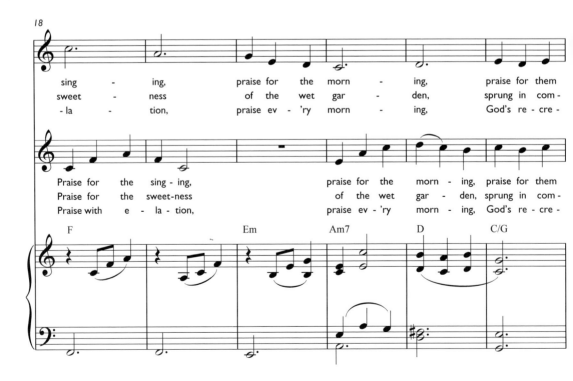

sing - ing, praise for the morn - ing, praise for them
sweet - ness of the wet gar - den, sprung in com -
- la - tion, praise ev - 'ry morn - ing, God's re - cre -

Praise for the sing - ing, praise for the morn - ing, praise for them
Praise for the sweet-ness of the wet gar - den, sprung in com -
Praise with e - la - tion, praise ev - 'ry morn - ing, God's re - cre -

F   Em   Am7   D   C/G

spring - ing fresh from the world.
plete - ness where his feet pass.
- a - tion of the new day.

spring - ing fresh from the world.
plete - ness where his feet pass.
- a - tion of the new day.

2. Sweet, the rain's world.
3. Mine is the
4. Morn-ing has

Nowhere Man

Words & Music by
John Lennon & Paul McCartney

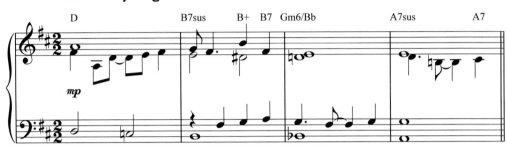

mak - ing all___ his No-where Plans_ for no-bo - dy.___
No-where Man__ can you see me___ at all?_____

mak - ing all___ his No-where Plans_ for no-bo - dy.___
No-where Man__ can you see me___ at all?_____

G · Gm · D · Dsus D C · Gsus G

Does - n't have a point of view, knows not where_ he's go - ing to.

Does - n't have a point of view, he knows not where_ he's go - ing to. Yes,

D · A · G · D A7/D D

Is-n't he___ a bit like you___ and me?_____ No - where / No - where

is-n't he___ a bit like you___ and me?_____

G   Em7b5   D   G/D   D   A/G

Man, please lis-ten, you don't know what_ you're miss-ing. No - where
Man, don't wor-ry, take your time, don't_ you hur - ry. Leave it

No-where Man, please lis - ten, don't know what_ you're miss-ing.
No-where Man, don't wor-ry, take your time,_ don't hur - ry.

F#m   G   D   A/G   F#m   G   D   A/G

Wouldn't It Be Nice

**Words & Music by
Brian Wilson, Tony Asher & Mike Love**

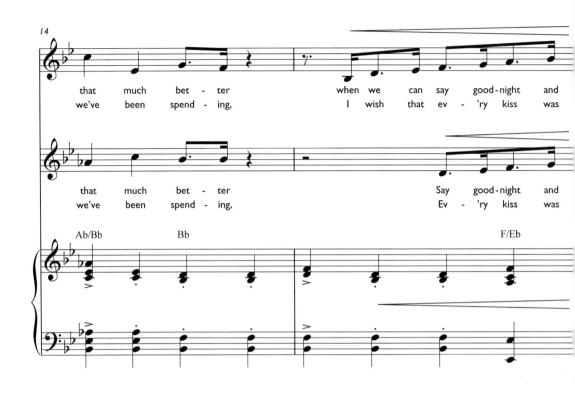

14

that much bet - ter   when we can say good - night and
we've been spend - ing,   I wish that ev - 'ry kiss was

that much bet - ter   Say good - night and
we've been spend - ing,   Ev - 'ry kiss was

Ab/Bb   Bb   F/Eb

16

stay   to - ge - ther._____   2. Would-n't it be
nev - er end - ing._____   Would-n't it be

stay,   stay to - ge - ther,_ stay____ to - ge - ther. 2. Would-n't it be
nev - er end - ing,_ nev - er end - ing. Would-n't it be

Dm7   Db7 Cm7 F7   Cm7   F7

28

nice? May - be if_____ we

nice? Would-n't it be nice? If we

Bb 3 G

decresc. mf

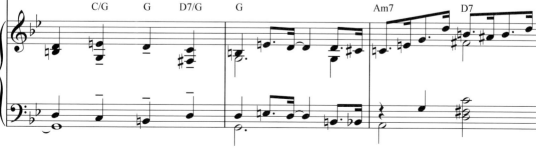

think and wish, and hope and pray, it might come true._

think and wish, and hope and pray, it might come true._ Yes, it might come true.

C/G G D7/G G Am7 D7

Ba - by then___ there would - n't be a sin - gle thing we could - n't do.___

Then there would - n't be a sin - gle thing we could - n't do.___

Oh, we could be mar - ried.___ and then we'd be hap -

We'd be mar - ried.___

Track Listing

1. I Have A Dream
(Andersson/Ulvaeus) Bocu Music Limited
Full Performance

2. Mr. Blue Sky
(Lynne) EMI Songs Limited
Full Performance

3. Morning Has Broken
(Farjeon/Stevens) Cat Music Limited
Full Performance

4. Nowhere Man
(Lennon/McCartney) Northern Songs
Full Performance

5. Wouldn't It Be Nice
(Wilson/Asher/Love) Rondor Music (London) Limited
Full Performance

6. I Have A Dream
(Andersson/Ulvaeus) Bocu Music Limited
Full Performance

7. Mr. Blue Sky
(Lynne) EMI Songs Limited
Full Performance

8. Morning Has Broken
(Farjeon/Stevens) Cat Music Limited
Full Performance

9. Nowhere Man
(Lennon/McCartney) Northern Songs
Full Performance

10. Wouldn't It Be Nice
(Wilson/Asher/Love) Rondor Music (London) Limited
Full Performance